/

MENOPAUSE
CONFIDENTIAL

MENOPAUSE CONFIDENTIAL

Usha Phadke

Book Guild Publishing
Sussex, England

First published in Great Britain in 2010 by
The Book Guild Ltd
Pavilion View
19 New Road
Brighton, BN1 1UF

Some of the reflections that appear in this book are amalgamations of my
interviews and discussions on the subject of the menopause. Individual names
and identifying characteristics have been changed. If you think you recognise
yourself in these pages the similarities are a coincidence unless I have received
your written permission to use your story.

Typesetting in Garamond by
Keyboard Services, Luton, Bedfordshire

Printed in Great Britain by
CPI Antony Rowe

A catalogue record for this book is available from
The British Library

ISBN 978 1 84624 471 1

I would like to thank the men and women who have opened their hearts and shared their most intimate thoughts with me. I am eternally grateful for their contribution. *Menopause Confidential* would not have been possible without their honesty.

Contents

MENOPAUSE CONFIDENTIAL

MENOPAUSE CONFIDENTIAL
MENOPAUSE CONFIDENTIAL

MENOPAUSE CONFIDENTIAL

Introduction

Let's be honest. Menopause is still a taboo subject. The mere mention of the word kills conversation. It is therefore hardly surprising that I was filled with trepidation when I decided to write *Menopause Confidential*. Was my decision to write about the views of women and men on the subject of the menopause a sign of how self-absorbed I had become? Was it because I was going through the menopause that I wanted to tell the whole world about it? Was I attention seeking? Should I not focus my energy on being one of the many women who 'just get on with this stage in life'? Should I join the ranks of the women who do not discuss something as personal as the menopause with other women or men? However, the more I thought about it and the more obstacles and challenges I encountered during my menopause, the more convinced I became that it is important for both women *and* men 'of a certain age' to talk openly about the subject.

This book of reflections is a product of my own experiences, and, more importantly, extensive discussions and interviews on the subject of the menopause. It incorporates the opinions and experiences of women and men between the ages of 49 and 83. My ambition is to encourage both sexes to develop a positive attitude to middle age and menopause. I want women to acknowledge that menopause is an integral part of life and nothing to be afraid of. I want more men to talk about how they feel and to admit that they could do with a little help in dealing with their partner's menopause.

My research revealed that women generally feel it is important to 'get on with *it*'. One lady told me that strong women do not indulge in self-pity or attention seeking. Another explained that she had so many other things to worry about during menopause that she had no time to think about how it was affecting her. Many felt that HRT (hormone replacement therapy) had been the answer for them. One of my close friends, however, remains convinced that HRT was responsible for her breast cancer.

Women who have been through or are going through menopause will confirm that the symptoms accompanying it can be painful to deal with. The vast majority of women have to face debilitating physical and psychological challenges due to the onset of menopause and treat this period in their life with stoicism. Most suffer in silence. This can often lead to a breakdown in communication with the man in their life and can sometimes result in a couple separating. Some women feel alienated from their partner and conclude that mid-life and menopause are things that they have to face on their own.

Some women view the menopause as something that has to be *defeated*: this very word implies that menopause is a battle, a war that has to be won (or lost). Most will agree, however, that on a human level there are invariably no 'winners' or 'losers' in a battle – just lots of casualties.

When talking about the menopause, I like to evoke the similarities between menopause and cohabitation with a partner. Anyone who has been in a relationship will agree that partners cannot always have what they want. In order to achieve equilibrium and create a harmonious coexistence during the menopause, it is important to appreciate and respect the menopause in all its guises. An open mind and a willingness to change or modify attitudes and behaviour, coupled with compromises along the way, will hopefully see most women and men through difficult times.

One of the women I interviewed was amused by my desire to write this book. 'I'm sure there's a lot of information *out there* on the menopause. Women can find it if they bother to look!' she said in a slightly dismissive voice. 'I'm not sure what your material can add to a subject that is already well documented. If you surf the Internet, you will find over a thousand books on the subject of the menopause! As for men, I don't think that they are in the slightest bit interested in the menopause. They will never understand what women have to go through. Men are programmed in a different way to women so you are probably wasting your time.'

My response to her was as follows: 'There may be a lot of *information* out there, but that doesn't mean that women are necessarily *better informed*! Besides, too much information can result in "information overload", and perhaps even hypochondria about the symptoms of menopause. Menopause is an important transition in a woman's life and is likely to be a challenge for the man in her life. Silence on the subject will not serve women well. Neither will it help women to change the mindset of the average man.'

I am probably stating the obvious, but I would like to remind women that life is never perfect. It is full of choices. Women have to accept that dealing with the menopause presents choices. Since it is a woman's body that is affected, it is *she* who needs to take control of her health in order to achieve a better quality of life during her menopause years. A woman can modify her lifestyle and nutrition, and search for greater 'balance' in all areas of her life. She can decide whether she wants to try HRT or complementary therapies. She can involve her husband or partner in times of need, she can exchange views on the menopause with him, or she can exclude him from her transition into her 'non-fertile' years. She can speak out if she feels that her doctor is not giving her the support she would like. Or she can 'go with the flow' and take no action at all, which is a choice in itself!

Men have choices too. They can bury their heads in the sand and pretend that the menopause is not happening, or they can learn more about it and try to help their partner live through it in a greater state of equilibrium. Most of the men I interviewed admitted that they are largely ignorant about the subject. Some felt that women are not sympathetic to the effect that their menopause has on the husband or partner. A few were brave enough to admit that men can also suffer from emotional and physical symptoms during middle age. One interviewee admitted that he was totally devastated when his wife left him for a younger man. He thinks that things might have turned out differently if he had told his wife that he was finding it difficult to cope with her menopause years, and that he too was struggling to come to terms with middle age. This man is now in a relationship with a woman who is half his age. He says she adores him and makes him feel young again! He says he intends to make sure that history does not repeat itself. A couple of men joked about the 'andropause' but seemed reluctant to take the conversation further. One man was of the opinion that the use of terms male menopause and andropause are misleading because men do not exhibit the plethora of physical symptoms which accompany a woman's 'loss of fertility' during menopause. He is right. Perhaps we should redefine andropause as the 'transition of a man into middle age'.

One of my aims in writing *Menopause Confidential* is to remind both women and men that menopause, like puberty and childbirth, is integral to life. We have been successful in teaching men how to support their partner during childbirth. There is no reason why we cannot be successful in educating men on how to support their partner during her menopause. While not all women will experience childbirth, all women will go through changes related to the menopause. So one could argue that the need to educate men about 'menopause matters' is even greater.

Men who are a product of the 'baby boom' generation seem willing to admit that equal opportunities between the sexes have left many men feeling insecure about their 'manhood' and their changing role in society. Our social structures do not encourage men of 'a certain age' to open up about their anxieties during middle age. Men feel embarrassed about expressing their thoughts, views and fears about growing old.

Women and men are not encouraged to feel good about becoming 'senior citizens'. Women are bombarded with advertisements about retaining a youthful appearance. They are applauded for 'looking young for their age' and having a body that belies their 'real age'. Men are indulged when they leave their wife of twenty years for a 'younger model'. Men live with different pressures. They are expected to remain 'successful'. They are often judged on their earning potential. Men are respected for their financial success, their profession and their status at work. So when a man reaches retirement age, he can end up feeling that he has lost his purpose in life. It is therefore understandable why so many women and men are reluctant to face the changes that inevitably accompany middle age and menopause.

Menopause need not become a topic that is hotly debated at a dinner party in mixed company, in the same way that one might discuss a recent holiday, climate change or perhaps the economy. As with any group discussion, topics that are debated have to be of interest to a majority of the audience present. There is, however, nothing wrong in women and men of a certain age taking the initiative and exchanging their experiences in a supportive and light-hearted manner. It need not become a discussion about *who is suffering the most* as a result of the menopause or *who is dealing with it more successfully* than others! Neither is it about winning the argument, being 'macho' or showing others that you are more knowledgeable about the subject than they are. The purpose of debate is to increase awareness of the menopause and remove the taboo that is associated with this subject.

The feminist movement has influenced the thinking of many women who were born in the latter half of the twentieth century. It has encouraged women to believe that there are few limits to what they can do with their life. Menopause, however, seems to remind a woman that 'it is not possible to have it all'. Menopause becomes a reminder that an enduring respect for the forces of Nature is just as important as the struggle for equal pay and equal opportunity.

In the United Kingdom, the campaign in favour of a greater awareness of the menopause is in its infancy. There is a focus on better primary health care for women but, in the case of menopause, the medical profession seems to focus on *treating the symptoms* of menopause rather than on *preparing* women (and men) for a healthy menopause. The medical profession should be encouraged to distribute separate fact sheets about the menopause to both women and men. The needs of men and women during the menopause years are different, so fact sheets would have to be tailored accordingly. Women should ask their Well Woman clinic and doctor to support menopause awareness classes. This might help women and couples through the unsettling times that usually accompany the menopause. The purpose of the classes would be to coach women (and hopefully men in due course) on how to address the physical and emotional changes that are associated with mid-life and menopause.

It is easy to be apathetic about issues that do not have a direct impact on our own life. It is easy to ignore the menopause if it does not affect us personally (many men seem to take this view), or because we have dealt with it in our own way (a view that many women seem to take). And for the vast majority of us, the passage of time enables us to 'forget' the menopause years. Why would we want to remember a phase in our life that we did not particularly enjoy? This way of thinking must change if women want to improve their health after the age of 50. It is vital to keep the menopause debate alive and in the public domain.

My book is not a critique of how cultural, religious, social, economic and literary attitudes over the centuries have influenced our attitudes towards the menopause. It does not offer advice on nutrition or the things that women can do to alleviate the physical symptoms of the menopause. My book is neither pro alternative therapies nor anti HRT. My aim is to encourage both sexes to formulate positive strategies and coping mechanisms for life during and after middle age. *Menopause Confidential* is about feelings towards the menopause. It is about individuals, change and hope, a reminder that, in the final analysis, it is individuals who are the instruments of change.

Every woman aspires to a better
quality of life

This is how she *feels*

Maya, 53

In my mid-40s, things started to change within me. I could feel it in my body and I could feel it in my head. It was hard to be specific about what exactly seemed to be changing. I was feeling more tired. The bags under my eyes were getting darker and more pronounced. But then, I have always suffered from dark circles under the eyes. And my skin usually turns pale during the winter months. My husband reminded me that I have never coped well with cold weather. A holiday in the sun or a good summer in the UK would probably work its normal magic.

During that time, I noticed that my periods had become much lighter and, on occasions, virtually non-existent. My doctor was of the view that I was a bit too young to start the menopause. I told my doctor that I was feeling run down and extremely tired. I had been on the Pill for nearly 20 years, so my doctor switched me on to a progesterone-only pill in the hope that this would alleviate some of my symptoms. It did not. I felt even worse than I had done before.

Yet another visit to the doctor's surgery revealed that I had low blood pressure. The doctor suggested that I change the dose of progesterone, commenting, 'I'm afraid it's a bit of a trial and error when it comes to determining the right dose of progesterone.'

As the months went by, I started to feel depressed. I often felt light-headed. Then my periods stopped completely.

My doctor asked me to consider my options: to switch to HRT, or use another method of contraception. I had been on the Pill for so long that I decided that maybe it was time to give my body a 'detox'. This would also give me time to research HRT. I had heard so many conflicting reports on the subject. A couple of my friends swore by it; others claimed that they were convinced their breast cancer had been triggered as a result of starting HRT.

HRT was such a dilemma for me. I had read that if you manage to fine-tune the correct dose for your body, it could work wonders. More energy, greater optimism about life and love and, best of all, more sex – something which our 50-something husbands would no doubt be very happy about!

Unable to make a decision, I did what most people do in the twenty-first century: I 'Googled' the word 'menopause'. And, probably like most other women who have done that, I was overwhelmed and baffled by the number of websites on the subject and by the information that was available. Pre-menopause, peri-menopause, menopause ... the endless stream of words made my eyes glaze over. What did it all mean for *me*?

So the next stop was amazon.co.uk, followed by visits to bookshops, largely because it seemed pointless (and expensive) buying books online without having had a quick browse through their content.

I tried talking to a neighbour about the menopause, but she seemed embarrassed and reluctant to respond to my remarks about how I found the start of menopause a 'liberating event'. No need to take precautions before sex. No need to carry tampons or sanitary towels. Less mess generally! My attempts at humour were greeted with nervous laughs. I spoke to a few older ladies at my golf club. They also seemed reluctant to chatter about something so personal. All they would say was, 'Yes, the hot flushes are the worst. And I do seem to have rather a lot of senior moments! But it does settle down eventually.' One lady told me that she had not suffered from 'all that'. 'I must have good genes,' she remarked. Most times, however, the conversation would swiftly move to 'safer' topics like 'the next holiday'.

I agonised about seeking another appointment with my doctor. After all, millions of women have been through the menopause. I felt self-indulgent about asking to see my doctor. Was I 'attention seeking' because I had started to feel a little depressed these days and sometimes tearful for no apparent reason? My libido was low, but perhaps that had something to do with the fact that my husband and I had been together for nearly 20 years. I reminded myself that the excitement and passion that a couple experiences in earlier years tends to diminish as work and family pressures leave their scars on both body and mind.

But, as the French would say, I was not *bien dans ma peau*. I could feel it. The rational side of me argued that I was entitled to seek an appointment with my doctor to discuss the menopause. 'A woman has to take responsibility for her body. She has to make sure that she is better informed. There is no need to suffer in silence. Women have a right to know what to expect during their "non-fertile" years.' This internal dialogue swirled through my head as my insomnia worsened and my night sweats left my husband complaining that he felt as though he was sleeping next to a furnace with wet sheets over it!

I longed for the support of a mother figure or the medical profession. I just wanted to hear the words, 'Don't worry. Menopause is a big change, like puberty. Don't be afraid. Embrace it and it will pass. These are the things that you need to do in order to come to terms with the physical and mental changes that are associated with this next phase in your life.' My husband commented that it was unfortunate that I could not talk to my mother about the menopause. I suppose many women *do* talk to their mothers – but I did not have that option.

I decided not to procrastinate any further, picked up the phone and asked for an appointment with the doctor. I was told that my doctor had retired, so I was allocated an appointment with my new doctor.

I was apprehensive as I sat in the waiting room. I silently rehearsed the questions that I would ask, reminding myself that I needed to use the correct terminology. Over the years, I have learned that if you don't ask the right questions, you don't get the right answers. As I walked into the doctor's room, my heart sank. My new doctor was young. Very young! All the questions that I had prepared evaporated. I stammered something about not being able to sleep these days, experiencing night sweats, feeling depressed and having a low sex drive. I can't remember much about our conversation, but the only thing that stuck in my head was the doctor recommending that my husband and I try more 'foreplay'. 'That will help your sex life. Why don't you try some "mood lighting"?' I looked at her in disbelief, mumbled something about HRT and wandered out of the room in a bit of a daze.

When I got back home I was really annoyed with myself. By the time my husband came home I was seething. 'What does a 24-year-old know about the menopause and how can she advise me on what to do?' I was both angry and frustrated.

A friend recommended that I see her doctor who, she felt, was more tuned into 'menopausal women'. The doctor was friendly and probably in her mid-30s. She suggested that it might be a good idea to have a 'body MOT', as she put it. I would have a blood test, my thyroid would be tested, etc., etc. The doctor did not ask if I had any other symptoms related to menopause and I felt too embarrassed to tell her that sexual intercourse had become very painful. The receptionist at the doctor's surgery rang me back two weeks later to say that my results were 'normal'. When I asked her about my hormone levels, she told me that my results suggested that I was probably 'entering the menopause years'. My visits to the doctor left me feeling irritated and dissatisfied.

So I decided to do what I normally do when I have a problem. I would read a 'self-help' book. I ended up reading numerous books. The two that seemed most relevant to me at the time were *Menopause* by Dr Miriam Stoppard[1] and a book called *Running and Walking for Women over 40: The Road to Sanity and Vanity*, by an American runner called Kathrine Switzer.[2]

I told myself that 'it was time to get a grip'. Both books extolled the virtues of exercise, a good diet and drinking less alcohol. I was conscious that my alcohol intake over the past twelve months had increased. I put it down to recent major upheavals in my life. I had celebrated my fiftieth birthday, left my job in the banking world to become a teacher, and my mother had passed away in India in less than satisfactory circumstances. I discovered that a glass of wine or two helped me to stay in the 'happy zone' for a lot longer.

By now, my weight had crept up by half a stone. I have always been hypersensitive about my weight. During my teenage years my cousins had given me the nickname 'Bessie Bunter'. I have never forgotten that. I was so fearful of putting on weight that I started to count calories. My weight seemed to stabilise on 1,400 calories a day, but my daily calorie allowance would soon be dwindled if I had two large glasses of wine in an evening. I started weighing all my food before cooking it. This irritated my husband who felt that I was showing the

[1] Dr Miriam Stoppard, *Menopause: The Complete Guide to Maintaining Health and Well-Being and Managing Your Life*, 2nd rev. ed. (London: Dorling Kindersley, 2001).

[2] Kathrine Switzer, *Running and Walking for Women over 40: The Road to Sanity and Vanity* (New York: St Martin's Press, 1998).

signs of obsessive compulsive disorder! He just didn't seem to get it. But that's not surprising because he has never had a problem with his weight and does not seem to be bothered that age might add a centimetre or two to his waistline. Miriam Stoppard's book rightly makes the point that when a woman reaches the age of menopause she needs to remember that a healthy weight is more important than staying a size 8!

Reading sensible advice is one thing. Putting it into practice and sticking with it is a completely different ball game! Nevertheless, reading books helped a lot. I decided that I would try to change my eating habits and take up running. I had read that a lot of women who had taken up running in their late 40s and early 50s said that it had changed their lives. Running increases endorphin levels and provides a mood boost. It also increases oestrogen levels in the body. I decided to combine running with a sensible low-fat diet consisting of plenty of vegetables, fruit, Omega 3 fish and small amounts of carbohydrates and protein. I cut back on my consumption of wine.

The first few weeks were hard, but I was determined to stick to my plan. However, because I have a goal-driven personality, I ignored the old adage of 'everything in moderation'. I ran a lot, but didn't eat enough carbohydrates. After several months I felt fitter, but did not feel better within myself. I would go to bed at 9.30 in the evening because I was tired. Sex became non-existent. By this stage I had given up alcohol completely. I am no taller than five foot and do not weigh a great deal, so a glass of wine was out of the question if I was planning a big run the next day. I was pleased with the way running had helped to reduce my night sweats. My weight was under control. I congratulated myself on the self-discipline I had demonstrated in changing my diet and exercise regime. But I could not understand why I would still often wake up in the

7

morning feeling depressed and sometimes even tearful. Even though I felt better physically, my mood swings were often unpredictable. I felt guilty that I had zero interest in sex. My husband was very supportive, but like most men, he found it difficult to express his feelings. From time to time he would get annoyed by my 'obsessive' behaviour, but put it down to that thing called the 'menopause'. At times he would say, 'Running seems to be working well for you, but maybe you're always tired because you're doing too much physical activity. Perhaps you should exercise less. It might make you feel better.'

I told myself that the bouts of depression and loss of libido would eventually pass. Take one day at a time. Try to be positive and, above all, keep occupied. Try not to think about the 'M' word!

By now, I was 51. I seemed to be coping better with the whole 'menopause thing'. This relative state of equilibrium was short lived, however. I managed to catch a severe urinary infection after a holiday in the sun with my husband. I rang the doctor's surgery, but this time round asked to see the oldest lady doctor! When I walked into the doctor's room I was relieved to see a grey-haired lady who looked as though she was in her mid-to-late 50s. We discussed the urinary infection and when I explained that I was suffering from severe vaginal dryness and had been using KY cream on holiday, she looked at me with a dead-pan face. In a dull and matter-of-fact voice, she explained that vaginal dryness was one of the symptoms of menopause. She explained that there are various creams on the market that can be used. 'Try one of the other creams. You can buy them over the counter at the pharmacy. That might help.'

She proceeded to lecture me on the importance of good hygiene and the need to avoid using bubble bath or soap when I was washing myself. I plucked up the courage to say that I had read somewhere that it was possible to get an oestrogen cream to alleviate the symptoms of vaginal dryness. 'There are vaginal creams, but I don't recommend them unless they are absolutely necessary.' I explained that I wanted to explore this route. She looked at me for a while and then wrote out a prescription. Being the cynical person I am, I wondered whether it was because my ten minutes were up, or whether she had concluded that I was the assertive and demanding type who would not take 'no' for an answer.

I went home with my medication, but without a real understanding of how it worked or what the side effects might be. When I had asked the doctor about side effects she had replied, 'All medicines of this nature have side effects if taken on a long-term basis.'

Having read the notes that accompanied the medication, I began to feel less confident about using it. Perhaps I was jumping the gun here. The doctor did not have much of a bedside manner, but perhaps she was right. 'Grin and bear it and it will pass.' But my biggest fear was the thought of getting another urinary infection. I had been in agony and did not relish the thought of going through that kind of pain again.

The medication did not have to be ingested and the doctor had said that I could stop taking it any time I wanted. I decided that the risk to my health was minimal. I was ready, both emotionally and physically, to try the medication, but wanted to get a second opinion. With encouragement from my husband, I contacted my local Well Woman clinic. The nurse and doctor made me feel at ease by telling me that I should not feel embarrassed about discussing sex and the menopause. The nurse said, 'We do nothing but talk about sex, so you've come to the right place!' The doctor was friendly and gave me the facts. She briefly outlined the implications of taking the prescription medicine and suggested that I try it for a while. She was also very diplomatic and suggested that I go back to my doctor if I needed further consultations. I came away feeling a lot happier – proof that a good bedside manner is important in the medical profession.

About six months later, as I was flicking through the satellite TV channels, I stumbled on a discussion about menopause on Oprah Winfrey's show. The programme consisted of a question-and-answer session with a doctor called Christiane Northrup. I was riveted by some of the things she discussed. I discovered that she had written a book called *The Wisdom of Menopause*.[3] I was so impressed by her that as soon as the programme ended I went online and bought a copy of her book.

The book contains a wealth of medical information and case studies, and the doctor shares her own experiences about menopause with the reader. I liked the frank and candid essays, anecdotes and recommendations. I asked my husband to read pages or chapters in the book that described the symptoms I was going through both physically and emotionally. This unconventional approach of mine helped him to acquire a better understanding of the menopause without feeling embarrassed or uncomfortable.

I was particularly impressed by Dr Northrup's knowledge of, and willingness to consider and embrace, 'alternative therapies'. She reminded the reader that cultural differences play an important part in how women deal with 'the menopause phase' of their life. I found her comments on 'self-cultivation' intriguing and fascinating. For example, by focusing your mind on different energy fields in your body, it is possible to stimulate certain parts of the female anatomy. I tried it and it helped me. I have found that, for it to work, this type of 'meditation' needs to be practised regularly and is not a one-off exercise.

[3] Dr Christiane Northrup, *The Wisdom of Menopause: The Complete Guide to Creating Physical and Emotional Health and Healing* (London: Piatkus, 2001).

The honesty with which Christiane Northrup discussed each aspect of the menopause made me realise that, while menopause is universal to all women of a certain age, each and every woman's experience of the menopause will be unique.

All women will go through menopause. Women do not have a choice in this matter. We cannot stop the biological clock – not for the foreseeable future, anyway. But like all things in life, women do have a choice about how to deal with this biological change. We can choose to be 'victims of menopause', or we can choose to embrace the menopause 'with wisdom'. The sad reality is that the arrival of the menopause in a woman's life is not celebrated. It tends to be seen as a scourge. It is also very much a taboo subject.

I feel that it is time for women to rally together and change this negative mindset. Should we not ask our doctor for a 'monthly menopause clinic'? Should we not invite husbands and partners to join such forums?

I am tempted to start a blog because I am frustrated by the lack of easily accessible support networks for women going through the menopause. I am also disappointed by the reluctance amongst women (even those who I know really well) to talk openly about the menopause. My husband is cautious about my blogging ambitions. He reminds me that blogs on the subject already exist, so would I really be adding anything of substance to the debate? 'Why don't you join one of the blogs that already exist?' he asks. 'They allow anonymity.' A friend has expressed concern that 'weirdos' might join my blog. She has also asked me if I 'really want to share intimate details about my menopause with complete strangers'. Her words of caution keep ringing in my head. Another acquaintance has suggested that it might be better to start a 'private blog'. Restricted access might encourage my friends to share their experiences of the menopause. I have now placed an order for

11

a book that teaches people how to create a blog – having decided that the first thing I need to do is to educate myself on blogging!

I turned 53 last month. I can see a glimmer of light at the end of the tunnel. My journey has not been easy and I am prepared for a few more twists and turns along the way. There are days when I don't feel great and I communicate that to my husband. I take one day at a time. I try to do everything in moderation, though it doesn't always work. If I have a bad day, I don't beat myself up about it. I remind myself that tomorrow is another day.

A friend of mine recently told me about the use of bio-identical hormones by women who are going through the menopause. Since my doctor probably does not have the time to explain things like that to me (not that I have the confidence to seek an appointment with her), I have ordered a book about bio-identical hormones. I hope it will not be riddled with medical jargon. Another thing on my 'To do List' is to find a good endocrinologist who I can talk to about HRT. I have no idea where to start. Neither do most other women that I have spoken to.

Writing about the menopause and discussing it with my friends has made me less embarrassed and less afraid of the menopause, largely because I feel I am better informed. I wonder if I will wake up one day and think, 'I feel as though the menopause is now over for me, and thanks to the menopause experience, I am a better person!'

Women are living much longer than they used to. We are better educated. We want a better quality of life. We want to be happier and more fulfilled as we reach our 50s. We are the generation that believes that life begins at 50.

So why is it that so many of us are still reluctant to talk openly about the menopause and share our experiences with other women and demand a better service from our doctor?

I think our mantra in respect of the menopause should be: 'A problem shared is a problem halved.'

Before you take something to relieve menopausal symptoms, acknowledge and listen to your body's inner wisdom in creating those outward symptoms. They are uniquely yours. How your hormones behave during peri-menopause and how your body and mind respond to hormonal changes is as personalised as your finger tips.

(Dr Christiane Northrup, *The Wisdom of Menopause*, p. 112)

Francesca, 59

I never enjoyed menstruation. It didn't make me proud to be a woman. It was painful, messy, irregular and often inconvenient. I was only grateful that I did not live in an era when you had to use old rags and wash them out instead of using tampons (or have the misfortune of being someone's maid and having to do the washing for the lady of the manor!). So in some ways, menopause was an event to look forward to, bringing freedom from the tyranny of pads, tampons, stomach cramps and accidents.

It came earlier than I had expected, in my late 40s. The gradual lengthening of time between periods and the shortening of their duration was a source of delight and relief. The hot flushes were to be expected, but I never found them to be overwhelming. Nevertheless, I wasn't sleeping well and was persuaded by a nurse at my doctor's surgery to try HRT. This worried me a little, as the use of HRT was still experimental at that time and studies had not been conducted for long enough to produce conclusive results about the side effects of long-term use. I felt as though we were effectively guinea pigs. Even so, I was persuaded by its potential benefits such as protection against osteoporosis, heart disease and depression and the promise of remaining youthful. I was given progesterone, which was said to reduce the risks of taking too much oestrogen.

In a way I felt cheated by the onset of menopause and the 'package' that comes with it. Menstruation was continuing, albeit in a shorter and more regular fashion. So when I read an article in a complementary health magazine about the growing incidence of cancer reported amongst HRT patients, I gave it up immediately. It wasn't a problem for me to give it up, since

14

I felt that I didn't need it in the first place. The surgery nurse wasn't pleased. Yet again, she ran through the benefits of HRT. Oestrogen keeps you young and prevents the side effects of menopause; it helps to prevent osteoporosis. I asked about the risks of cancer. She thought there might be just a small risk, especially if there was a history of cancer in the family. Did the risk of cancer outweigh the benefits of not getting osteoporosis? Well actually, it did, especially as there had been cancer in the family but not osteoporosis. It was my choice, but I felt a bit browbeaten by the nurse.

Rightly or wrongly, I felt that there was some sort of 'agenda' going on to get as many women as possible on HRT – all grist for the scientific mill and the pharmaceutical companies, but without being upfront and honest that this was the case. I felt that the drive to get more and more menopausal women on HRT was irresponsible and unethical. I therefore had no qualms about giving up HRT. Besides, my preference has always been for complementary treatment where possible. That is not to say that I don't appreciate the benefits of modern allopathic medicine and the wonderful treatments that are available to us these days, most of which I would not refuse to take if I was suffering from a serious illness. However, modern medicines do have side effects and focus principally on treating symptoms. They tend to focus on treating one aspect or system of the body, which may throw the rest of the body out of balance, thereby requiring further medicine to balance things out.

While mainstream medicine plays a vital role in our well-being, I feel that complementary treatments can provide good back-up and support for modern medicine, often relieving side effects and sometimes bringing relief entirely on their own.

So when I went to the doctor again for vaginal dryness and was given an oestrogen cream, I was apprehensive. If the hormones in HRT could give you cancer, what would the oestrogen in the cream do to me? I was probably being a bit paranoid, but my gut feeling was to ditch the cream.

There are now alternatives to oestrogen creams and HRT. These products, which I like to refer to as 'supplements', do not contain chemicals or synthetic compounds. They have names like Eros, Sylk, Mulla Mulla, She Oak, Billy Goat Plum and Yes, which make me just giggle in amusement.

A personal favourite of mine are the Flower essences. I feel that they are very subtle in the way they work and can take some time to have an effect. I admit that there may be some truth in the claim that these products only work because our mind is 'open' to them, and because there is an emotional and psychological willingness to embrace them.

I understand that, more recently, there is a school of thought that natural progesterone has replaced oestrogen as the hormone that solves all our menopause problems and keeps us young. Articles for and against the use of natural progesterone can be found on websites such as www.positivehealth.com. *Positive Health* is a specialist rather than a popular journal. It discusses natural complementary remedies of all kinds, including those for women's issues such as menopause. Research programmes are presented and discussed in this publication. I have found them particularly interesting, but they tend to be controversial because the majority of the public, and especially the medical profession, think of complementary therapies as airy-fairy and anecdotal.

One of the articles on the subject of alternative therapies that particularly impressed me is written by Marilyn Glenville, who writes about women's issues. She argues against the use of natural progesterone as a modern panacea for menopausal women. Glenville gives advice on nutrition and promotes a range of vitamin products created especially for particular problems such as fat around the midriff, osteoporosis and menopause. She has also written books about these subjects.

But let's get back to my own story. As time went on, I began to put on weight even though I was eating the same as usual. A few days' or even a few weeks' dieting didn't shift the pounds in the way that it had in past years. Over a period of ten years, my weight increased from eight and a half stone to ten stone, where it seemed to settle and stabilise. But my arms became flabby, so I couldn't wear short sleeves. My waist measurement increased such that I felt as though I had become a middle-aged apple instead of a youthful English pear! Tight-fitting tops and skirts were out – loose cardigans were in. I've recently lost a few pounds, mainly by giving up bread and biscuits, but the pounds don't seem to have come off my stomach.

The other bad thing that happened to me because of the menopause was the gradual erosion of memory. I've always been bad at remembering names, so at first it seemed normal to be forgetful. But I began to forget appointments and couldn't remember what people had said to me from one week to the next, sometimes from one day to the next. I couldn't think of the words I needed and sometimes could barely string them together into a sentence. Things would get lost and couldn't be found. There was constant confusion. This has carried on to the present day. There could be other reasons for this state of mind: stress, not enough sleep, not drinking enough water, advancing age, perhaps even early signs of dementia. All these things have crossed my mind, but rather than implement strategies to deal with this mental state, I blame it on the menopause. It is comforting to know that many of my younger and menopausal friends share similar difficulties. Surely, at the end of the day, all menopausal women can't be suffering from dementia, can they? So there must be another explanation. Is it lifestyle, diet, genetic? What I would like to do is to find the cause so that I can make a decision on how I can treat the symptom.

There are many who argue that for some women who are on HRT, progesterone does not act like progesterone, but compounds problems by giving women more oestrogen than they need, thereby causing the very problems that HRT is supposed to prevent.

All in all, I think I've got off fairly lightly, although I *have* developed osteopenia, a precursor to osteoporosis. I don't know why this should be. It doesn't run in the family and my diet has always contained plenty of calcium and magnesium. I have been told that our bone-density formation is at its maximum between the ages of 25 and 30. In the years of maximum bone-density formation I lived in places where there was plenty of sunshine, so I had enough Vitamin D. Could my osteopenia therefore have been caused by taking progesterone for a year? It could also be that I was unaware at the time that calcium alone is not enough to maintain strong bones. A diet and supplements that are rich in magnesium, Vitamins D and K and boron are also necessary. It also helps to know that calcium and magnesium should be the citrate form, which is highly absorbable, rather than the carbonate form.

I have now been prescribed alendronic acid. The very name fills me with apprehension. It works by preventing calcium leaching out of the bones. It apparently also reduces the risk of fractures by 50 per cent, which has to be a good thing. I take one tablet once a week, first thing in the morning, with a large glass of water. I have to stay upright for at least half an hour and not eat or drink anything until the half hour is up. My doctor has said that new drugs are coming out all the time and that, when enough research has been done, he will prescribe me something which allows new growth in the bones. So, on that basis, I consider myself lucky. Meanwhile, I take supplements for osteoporosis and follow specialist advice regarding dietary changes and exercise.

The menopause seems to be a subject that we don't like talking about apart from the odd joke about hot flushes. In all my years as a counsellor (now retired), the menopause was rarely presented as a primary issue for concern. It was often categorised as just one more thing to worry about, adding to all the other problems and burdens of life. It was not regarded as something to be focused on in its own right. It often served as a useful hook for husbands on which to hang their wives' depression and dissatisfaction with life, relieving them of the necessity to look at their own contribution to marital discord. As regards the female clients who came to see me, their issues were generally other than those brought on by the menopause. On reflection, it could well be that symptoms which were considered by the doctor to be menopausal were referred to the practice nurse or a Well Woman clinic. The latter seems to be the first place where women are sent for 'sex-related issues'.

There are, of course, huge 'losses' for women at the time of menopause – loss of youth, attractiveness, energy, fertility, the end of the road for women who have been desperate to conceive but have been unable to, difficulties with sex, fear of ageing and illness, fear of abandonment, children moving away from home. No wonder women get depressed. It's the time when we begin to lose our value in a youth-obsessed society and culture.

Both the medical profession and 'ordinary' counsellors have a role in helping women (and men) through the menopause. The latter focus on listening, understanding body language, creating a safe place for the client/patient to talk, being genuine and empathetic, and so on.

These days, some nurses do have training in 'specialist'

counselling skills. It would be a good thing if this was more widespread, especially in Well Woman clinics where women are subject to embarrassing procedures and often find it difficult to talk about sexual problems associated with the menopause.

Just as nurses would benefit from more training on counselling women who are going through the menopause, more training could be made available for 'ordinary' counsellors on the emotional problems relating to the menopause. This would enable doctors and practice nurses to refer women who require longer-term emotional counselling to other qualified members of the counselling fraternity. However, if the symptoms are purely a result of hormonal imbalances, then the counselling would have to be of a primarily practical and advisory nature, involving a dispensing of information and remedies, advice on nutrition, life balance, relaxation, exercise, and so on.

That is not what ordinary counsellors currently do. You can talk to a counsellor about how the menopause makes you feel, but the ideal person to talk to, in my mind, would be a specialist nurse with some medical knowledge, general counselling training and loads of empathy for the patient.

I think that, at the end of the day, women have to take responsibility and make informed *choices*. We should question all forms of treatment, both traditional and complementary, study the research and accept what we feel will be the most helpful to us individually. When we can make informed decisions about our own health and take action accordingly, we will feel more in control of our lives.

The longer we keep menopause in the closet or pretend it's nothing to get excited about, the longer we perpetuate the ignorance and veil of myths surrounding it. The central myth is that menopause is a time in a woman's life when she goes batty for a few years – subject to wild rages and deep depressions – and after it she mourns her lost youth and fades into the woodwork. In truth, menopause is a bridge to the most vital and liberated period in a woman's life.

(Gail Sheehy, *The Silent Passage*,[4] p. 6)

---

[4] Gail Sheehy, *The Silent Passage* (New York: Pocket Books, 1993).

Carla, 61

At the age of 44 I had two serious operations which resulted in my ovaries being removed. I was forced to stay in hospital for six weeks. I was in a lot of pain and physically weak. The whole process seemed endless, leaving me to question what quality of life I would have when I returned home. At my lowest point, I felt that I would never be able to lead a normal life again. The vision of my husband and children kept me going. How would they feel? How would they cope if I did not pull through this? I wanted to see my children grow up and blossom into young adults. I wanted to share in their success and be there to support them during challenging times.

I often think that I survived because I am one of those individuals whose glass is always half full! I probably owe this to the way my parents brought me up.

You might be thinking, 'What does all that have to do with the menopause?'

The removal of my ovaries meant that there was no 'transition' into the menopause years. I was put on HRT as soon as my ovaries were removed and stayed on it until the age of 60. I did not have the luxury of choice regarding HRT. I was told I had to take it because of the operation I had undergone. Hot flushes, night sweats, mood swings, depression – all the ailments that menopausal women complain about – did not affect me. During my 50s, I also experienced gall bladder and bowel problems. I was forced to change my diet and cut out certain types of food. These enforced changes to my diet may have helped me during my menopause years.

When I look back at the past decade, I can see that one of

the main things that helped me to achieve more balance in my life was my attitude to life in general. I believe that life *is* too short and we should therefore make the most of it.

It is important to have a positive attitude to challenges in life. This includes the menopause. Life is never perfect. While it is important to make informed judgements about issues and problems, over-intellectualisation, endless introspection and self-analysis can be detrimental to our well-being.

Modern life imposes increasing levels of pressure on women. Magazines and advertisements give us the subliminal message that we can never be too thin or too rich. What we don't hear on a daily basis is that women can't 'have it all', we will *all* become old and frail one day, and achieving balance in all aspects of your life as you get older is important. So is good self-esteem.

We live in a culture where there is information overload. Too much information and knowledge can be counterproductive. The number of lifestyle choices that are available to the modern woman can lead to confusion and disappointment.

I feel that many women forget that it is important to get things into perspective as we enter our menopause years. Menopause causes the body to change. We have to learn to accept the physical changes that accompany menopause. Our waist measurement will increase slightly, so regular exercise is essential. We will feel the effects of the decreasing levels of oestrogen. We therefore need to focus on our diet and lifestyle. I feel that women need to learn and, more importantly, be taught how to manage their health well in advance of the menopause.

I have now given up HRT because I do not seem to have the need for it. I try to eat well. I keep occupied and do a lot of fundraising. It gives me a sense of purpose to know that I am helping other people and children in particular. I have a good and active social life. If I get tired, I rest.

I sometimes think that perhaps I am just a very lucky woman. I am in a good, stable and happy marriage. I have never felt the need for sympathy (even during my time in hospital) and as I get older, I am hugely appreciative of the support I get from my family and friends. I like who I see in the mirror every morning! I was put on HRT at a relatively young age, so I did not suffer the 'normal' symptoms related to the menopause. I am thankful for that. There has recently been a lot of negative press about HRT. Women need to be better educated about HRT so they can make an informed decision on whether or not to use it.

My philosophy on life is as follows. Life is never plain sailing. Neither is menopause. We learn as we go along. The important thing is to be passionate about whatever activity you choose to do and get on with your life in a positive state of mind.

Attitude is a little thing that makes a big difference.

(Winston Churchill)

Clare, 62

My first inkling that life might change as one got older came when I was about 13. This was when my periods started. My mother was around 50 at the time. Suddenly she would explode, there would be a great deal of noise and activity as she tore off outer garments and flung open windows. This was particularly noticeable when we were out on a family jaunt in the car. As children, sitting in the back, we would suddenly be blasted by cold air and there would be loud complaints. My father, always the driver, would sit there impassively. It always seemed to be his fault!

When I came to understand the situation better, I vowed that when my time came for 'the change', I would not make such a song and dance about it. Why did my menopause need to affect anyone else?

My menopause came on by stealth. Coming up to 50, I had given up the Pill and was using a coil for contraception. Having at least one friend who had suddenly become pregnant at 50 and found herself with a new baby just as her other children were looking independent, I had decided this was something that I definitely had to avoid. One day my coil just popped out. I was still having very heavy periods. I tried to get one of the new Mirena coils fitted. These were expensive and, with a retroverted uterus, I was a difficult case. At the Family Planning clinic one of the doctors suggested a blood test to see whether I was still fertile. What a brilliant idea! All the uncertainty would be gone and, in fact, it was found that I no longer needed contraception at all. Why is this not offered to all women at the age of 50? It seems to me a good way to know where you stand at this critical stage of life.

25

During puberty I had very heavy and painful periods. My father was a doctor and his advice for everything was 'have an aspirin and lie down for a bit'. For days at a time I was topped up with aspirin – until I learned about its bad effects on the stomach. My excessive use of aspirin may explain my problems in that area during the menopause. When the monthly periods finally stopped, it was a great relief. I rejoiced in not having to be careful about what I wore or what activity I did.

Of course, it was suggested to me that I should start HRT as a way to protect my heart and bones. All the young, up-to-date, female doctors I was seeing at this stage (and there seemed to be several of them) thought it was a no-brainer. So I started with the patches and felt good.

About five years later, when the scare stories started to come through, I decided that perhaps I had been on HRT long enough and would stop. I had not started it to prevent any symptoms and might not notice any difference. How wrong I was! From that time, I began to get the hot flushes and night sweats.

Well, at least I did not mimic my mother with her abandoned displays of frustration, but I did gently steam! From that time I stopped wearing woollen sweaters and opted for easily removable garments. To this day, ten years on, just as I think my body has calmed down, I can still be caught by a hot flush. I think they come when I am very tired or emotionally upset. My husband often seems to be around at the time and I am invariably fighting for my voice to be heard! It seems to me that I have been quite a compliant wife, always giving way to the wishes of others for the sake of a quiet life. Again my mother seems to have had a lot to do with this! She was a difficult woman, riding rough-shod over others in her insistence not to be a 'doormat'. She always got her own way, or everyone suffered from her abrasive tongue. My poor father was reduced to silence. I am determined not to be like my mother!

Having had the wonderful opportunity to stay at home and bring up my children, my life was centred round them and keeping the home running smoothly for my husband. I did go back to work part-time when my youngest child was five and started school, but my husband was the chief breadwinner so my role of 'stay-at-home mum and wife' was of paramount importance. I accepted this duty and learned to keep quiet about any frustrations I had about life. I subdued my wishes to the greater needs of the family. Then I reached the menopause and realised that I no longer knew what it was that I wanted from life!

So now that I have faced the menopause and my children have grown up and moved out, I have freedom. But what do I want to do with it? In fact, life has continued much as before. I try to keep the status quo, but at the same time I feel an increasing desire to do things and see things 'before it is too late'. Many of the things that seemed important when I was younger no longer seem relevant. My children no longer need me, although, as the grandchildren have started to come along, I will have a role as a grandmother and that I will enjoy. But I do feel this is *my* time and I should take it back. It is not a time to tie myself down as a permanent 'carer' for others. I want to declutter my life and concentrate on what I feel are the essentials.

Having elderly relatives is also proving difficult. This time for myself is coinciding with demands on my time from them and, selfishly, I resent that my time is being stolen. I feel that this is a time for my husband and me to get back to the days of our early marriage, before the children came along, when we were important to each other and had time for each other. My husband is bogged down in the final phase of his working life and the constant sense of obligation that his large family of older relatives has instilled in him. It has always caused friction between us, because I feel that his wife and children should come first. Perhaps some cunning stratagem is needed here to work out a timetable to meet all needs.

In the meantime, I am left wondering if the menopause has made me less tolerant. But perhaps it has given me the wisdom and strength to admit that from time to time both my husband and I need to give priority to *my* needs in life. I do not see this as being selfish. It is just an acknowledgement of the fact that balancing our individual needs is important as we get older.

A smile, a greeting and a helping hand make the world a better place, particularly when one is going through the menopause.

(author unknown)

Liz, 72

I recently came off HRT after having taken it for 18 years. It was my wish to do so, but my doctor was very supportive and agreed that it was probably the right decision because I had been on HRT for such a long time. I think my decision to say a final goodbye to HRT was influenced by my advancing age, slightly higher blood pressure and current recommendations from the NHS (National Health Service) that women should only take HRT for up to five years.

I took my first dose of HRT at the age of 54. I was feeling both unwell and depressed.

Depression was something that I had become used to. I started suffering from severe depression at the age of 41. The depression coincided with my marriage breaking up. I took an anti-depressant drug for over ten years because without it, I would not have been able to function properly. I decided to start HRT because I found the hot flushes totally debilitating. I was conscious that taking both HRT and anti-depressants at the same time was making me more and more dependent on medication. However, it seemed a small price to pay if it allowed me to get through each day.

An accidental meeting with a doctor and continued counselling sessions led me to my decision to stop taking anti-depressants a couple of months after starting HRT.

It took six months for my body to adjust to this change. During that time, I continued to feel unwell. Hot flushes continued to plague me. I started to suffer from mood swings and anxiety attacks. I was working in an upmarket department store at the time. The severity of my symptoms finally forced me to give up my job. I ended up staying at home for two years. I did not feel in control. I felt as though I needed some space to sort myself out. Looking back on that time, I understand that going on HRT and coming off anti-depressants soon after probably put a huge strain on me, both physically and emotionally. I should have given myself more time to come off the anti-depressants.

I eventually felt well enough to go back to work. My body seemed to be responding well to HRT. I was not afraid to take HRT, even though my mother had suffered from breast cancer. She had never taken any medication in her life and still developed cancer. In my day there was scant information available to women on the side effects related to HRT. So, given the positive reports from the medical profession about the benefits of HRT, I had no qualms about taking it.

HRT made me feel better. Like a lot of other women, I had to try several different types in order to identify one that suited me the most. Changing the type of HRT that I was using caused some ups and downs, but not to the extent that I felt I could not function properly on a daily basis.

During that time of change, my periods and hot flushes continued. As I approached my 57th birthday, I had my last bleed on HRT; final confirmation that I was now in the non-fertile stage of my life. I toyed with the idea of stopping HRT. But every time I did, the hot flushes came back with a vengeance. My doctor eventually recommended a different type of HRT which was new to the market. My doctor and I were both pleased and relieved to discover that this particular HRT turned out to be the right one for me. I was thrilled. The hot flushes disappeared. I felt I could cope with working until I was 60 and well beyond if I wished! For the first time in a long time, I felt I had more balance and control in my life. I was much happier.

I have had no regrets about taking HRT for so many years. It was the prop I needed for a better quality of life. I am not afraid that I may have increased my chances of developing breast cancer. I continue to have regular medical check-ups. I follow a sensible diet. I watch my weight. I try my best to keep fit.

I am close to my children and grandchildren. I hope my time with them will teach them that life is never perfect, even though the celebrity culture that surrounds us would have us believe otherwise. Having money certainly helps, but money cannot buy happiness or good health.

Women cannot, and should not, fight the ageing process. We should not fear becoming 'old and wrinkly'. We should not fear physical change. We should not fear the menopause. We should not fear the use of HRT.

We should learn to respect the changes that accompany menopause. We should deal with them as sensibly as we possibly can! We sometimes make wrong choices in life and have to learn to live with the consequences. That's life!

I believe that the onset of menopause is designed to increase a woman's spiritual awareness of the powerful forces of Mother Nature. As I age, I am becoming acutely aware of my own mortality. I have started to wonder why a woman's ovaries stop producing eggs around the age of 50. Why do some people have so much in life and others so little? Why do nations still go to war? Why do we not learn from our mistakes? Why? Why? Why?

I smile to myself because 'Why?' is the question that my young grandchildren ask me. Decades of experience have taught me that some things in life will remain a mystery.

But that, of course, is not the response that I give to my grandchildren!

Our first step in wisdom is to question everything – and our last is to come to terms with everything.

(George C. Lichtenberg)

Edith, 83

The menopause has become a dim and distant memory for me. There is one thing, however, that I can clearly remember about that time in my life. Everything seemed very hectic. My parents lived locally and needed help. My mother was suffering from the early onset of Alzheimer's. Both my children were at school and going through their teenage years. One of my sons had a few health problems as a result of having had meningitis as a baby. I worked part-time. I always felt under pressure.

In my late 40s I noticed that my periods were becoming lighter and less frequent. I seem to remember that my periods stopped completely a year or two later. I only remember one instance of suffering from a hot flush, and I put down feelings of tiredness, occasional depression or other health problems to my lifestyle and personal circumstances. I did not attribute such ailments to the menopause. I did not consult a doctor or take any medication apart from the odd Disprin. My husband and I continued to enjoy our sexual relationship, so no problems there!

One odd thing that seems to have continued to this day, despite my advanced age, is the fact that roughly every four weeks I notice that I feel stressed and unbalanced for a day or two for no apparent reason. And I tend to suffer from constipation! These symptoms remind me of my younger days and premenstrual times, although these were never debilitating in my case.

I had a happy childhood even though I was separated from my mother and father for long periods due to my father's work, which took him to exotic places like India. I have always been independent in nature. I went to boarding school and trained as a physiotherapist. I understand my body and try, to this day, to treat it well, both physically and emotionally.

My friends and I sometimes chatter about our menopause experiences. As you have probably gathered by now, I am not one of those women who suffered as a result of the menopause. I have no idea why that should be. I feel sorry for all those women who experience physical and emotional turmoil during the menopause. It was not a problem for me!

I am sure there are lots of women out there like me. I hope my daughter will be one of them. My friends think that my genetic make-up, my upbringing and my financial security are responsible for my good health and positive outlook on life. I would add strength of character and self-discipline to that list! It is not just a question of the circumstances that one is born into. The choices that an individual makes in life are equally relevant.

If your body's not right, the rest of your day will go wrong. Take care of yourself.

(V.L. Allineare)

Things your mother should have told you when you turned 40!

- Don't be afraid of the menopause. Prepare yourself both physically and mentally for it. Don't take the attitude 'Why worry about something before it happens?'

- The hormonal changes you experience during menopause will be as monumental as the changes you went through during puberty.

- Educate yourself about the terms pre-menopause, peri-menopause, menopause and post menopause. Do your research. Demand a better service from you doctor.

- You are unique. One glove does not fit all. The strategies and coping mechanisms that work for some women may not work for you.

- You will become what you eat. Focus on a healthy menopause not a 'thin' menopause.

- Make exercise and 'sexercise' a priority in your life.

- If you reach the stage where you'd rather have a passion fruit smoothie than sex, seek help!

- Talk to your partner about menopause and sex. You may go off sex during menopause but he won't.

- If you suffer from vaginal dryness, don't be embarrassed to seek help.

- Tell the man in your life how you feel. Educate him about the menopause.

- Ask your partner for his opinion on menopause and HRT. Ask him if he is worried about mid-life.

- Dealing with the physical and emotional aspects of menopause will require effort.

- Find purpose in your life other than your children and your partner.

- There is no such thing as a perfect menopause experience. The road to happiness during middle age depends on your perception of what is perfect.

- Listen to your body.

- Don't be a martyr. Don't suffer in silence.

- Menopause is normal. Don't be embarrassed to talk about it.

Books for her

Greer, Germaine, *The Change: Women, Aging and the Menopause* (New York: Ballantine, 1993).

McGraw, Robin, *What's Age got to do with it?* (Nashville Tennessee: Thomas Nelson, 2009).

Northrup, Dr Christiane, *The Wisdom of Menopause: The Complete Guide to Creating Physical and Emotional Health and Healing* (London: Piatkus, 2001).

Platt, Michael E., *The Miracle of Bio-identical Hormones* (California: Clancy Lane Publishing, 2008).

Somers, Suzanne, *The Sexy Years: Discover the Hormone Connection: The Secret to Fabulous Sex, Great Health and Vitality, for Women and Men* (New York: Three Rivers Press, 2005).

Her menopause. My challenge!

This is how he *really feels*

Michael, 49

I hope my views on the menopause will not offend my partner or other female readers. Like many men, I am not very good at talking about my emotions.

One of my excuses is that I don't have the time to focus on my emotions. I am under a lot of pressure at work. I find the daily commute into work quite exhausting. My job involves overseas travel. I have limited spare time, so thinking about issues like my partner's menopause is not on my list of priorities.

At weekends (unlike my partner, who, by the way is five years older than me) I prefer to have a lie in (something that is becoming less frequent these days, because my partner tends to get up early and has the ability to make me feel guilty about staying in bed!). In my free time, I like to go to the gym, play golf or watch a sports event on the TV. I like to read a car magazine, the *Economist*, or a specialist magazine on finance. I bought a motorbike six months ago. My friends and I sometimes go away for a biking weekend.

I have become aware that my other half is often moody, frequently unreasonable and nags me unnecessarily. I would probably go so far as to admit that a 'discord' is manifesting itself in several areas of our life. My partner tends to lose it if I don't share in some of the household chores like the gardening, shopping and cooking. But she is going through the menopause, so I have to grin and bear it!

She has become picky about the food she eats. She is often hyperactive first thing in the morning, but runs out of energy by six in the evening. She seems unnecessarily focused on forward planning all our activities, while I just prefer to go with the flow. Unlike me, my partner of ten years is very focused in her attitude towards life. That is what attracted me to her. That, and her independence, both financial and emotional. So it has come as a bit of a shock to me that she is having difficulty in exercising control over her emotions.

In recent months, she has thrown me off balance by probing me on my feelings about our relationship and my opinion on how I feel things have changed since her menopause started three years ago. She seems to have made it her mission to keep me up to date on her research on the menopause and, more importantly, on the steps that she is taking to deal with her symptoms, both physical and emotional. She is very open about her problems and frustrations and the lack of tangible support from her doctor on the subject. This has reminded me that I need to try a little harder to understand what she might be going through.

My partner's desire to keep me informed about her challenges with the menopause has made me realise just how ignorant I am about the subject. To me, the menopause is a sign that a woman has reached her non-fertile years and will stop having periods, and babies of course. I have heard that a woman can have 'funny turns' from time to time and get cranky when she is going through the menopause. I gained this little insight from an awkward conversation I had with my father in the pub the other day. He seemed embarrassed when I told him that my partner was struggling with the menopause, so I did not ask him how he had coped with my mother's 'funny turns'!

While I do not have much of a clue about the menopause, there is one thing of which I have become acutely aware. Sex seems to be virtually non-existent these days. My partner sweats profusely at night. This is particularly annoying because all the bedclothes get soggy in the middle of the night. She will toss and turn, making it difficult for me to get a good night's sleep. Either she or I often resort to sleeping in different bedrooms.

I have to confess that if my partner did not keep the debate about her menopause alive, I would do what I have usually done when faced with a situation that I cannot control: switch off and ignore it!

My partner's quest for improved health, her desire to achieve a better quality of life and her struggle for greater balance in our relationship has prompted me to explore my own feelings about the menopause and mid-life. I would like to be supportive of my partner during her menopause, but I am not ashamed to admit that I am really not that interested in the topic.

The whole thing seems so complicated. It is unclear to me whether her mood swings are worse because of the menopause, or whether her current volatility can be attributed to life events such as her career, her upbringing, the fact that she has never had children (and now can't), her childhood experiences or her continuing struggle to achieve better self-esteem and recognition, all aggravated because she is conscious that she is getting older.

Could it be that the menopause has cranked up my partner's goal-driven personality and her desire to constantly seek a new challenge? Or is it that, after having lived with each other for a decade, we have both reached a stage where we need to fine tune our individual and collective hopes and aspirations for the years that lie ahead of us? I am asking myself a lot of questions, but I do not seem to have all the answers.

My partner and I have always enjoyed great sex. But this has changed. Has she lost interest in me? She tells me that I can blame the physical and hormonal changes that she is going through for her low libido. Perhaps I am not trying hard enough to please her. I admit that I am not a hugely romantic person. I do not buy flowers and spend lots of money in order to 'woo' her. My partner has never expected this type of pampering in the past, so I don't see why that should change just because she is going through the menopause.

Discussions with my partner about her menopause have given me a better understanding of why some men of a certain age leave their wives for a 'younger model'. A younger woman embarking on a new relationship is likely to be better at feeding a man's ego and, above all, probably has more energy and is therefore willing to indulge in lots of sex. A younger woman probably makes an older man feel young again.

If I were to pick two words to describe my feelings towards the menopause, they would be 'frustration' and 'helplessness'. Frustration because my partner's menopause has impacted on our sex life, and helplessness because I see the pain and discomfort that she has to go through.

My partner has decided that she does not want to take HRT in order to alleviate some of the physical symptoms of the menopause. I support her fully in this decision. It is *her* body and it is therefore up to her to make that choice.

We sometimes discuss the pros and cons of HRT. I am becoming more familiar with terminology like hypothyroidism and osteopenia. I think it would be helpful for someone like me to have more information and support on the subject of the menopause from my doctor. I believe that a simple and succinct fact sheet on the menopause that is aimed at men would be a great help. I suppose I should ask my doctor if such a thing exists. But to be honest, I can't see myself seeking an appointment with my doctor to discuss my partner's menopause!

I have come to the conclusion that it is important for a man whose wife or partner is going through the menopause to understand what to expect. Men and women may cope better if they are prepared for 'the change'.

It has been difficult for me to give my partner support at this critical time in her life. Why? Because I have not been educated about the subject and no one has prepared me for life with my partner during her non-fertile years.

Our society has made a lot of progress in preparing a man for childbirth. I feel that a man also needs to prepare for the time when the woman in his life will go through the menopause.

I now make it a point at the end of each day to ask my partner how she is feeling. I can tell when she is in one of her 'moods', because she replies, 'I'm *fine*,' in a somewhat aggressive tone of voice. It reminds me of the conversation between Donald Sutherland and Mark Wahlberg in the film *The Italian Job*. For those of you who have not seen the film, FINE stands for 'Freaked out, Insecure, Neurotic and Emotional'. Perhaps I will wait until this 'menopause thing' is over before I joke about this acronym with my partner…

My partner surprised me the other day by telling me that it is equally important for women to acknowledge that there may be such a thing as 'andropause'. It is a term that Americans like to use to describe the male menopause. I guess most men prefer to use the words 'mid-life crisis'. It would appear that the things my partner might have to contend with during my 'andropause' years are a drop in my energy levels, my libido and my stamina and a decline in my *joie de vivre*. Or is that a polite way of saying that I may turn into a grumpy old man? If I don't have a sensible diet and follow an exercise regime, I will undoubtedly have to face the prospect of weight gain around the waist. I have to confess that the symptoms of 'andropause' do not sound as bad as hot flushes, night sweats, erratic periods, vaginal dryness, urinary infections and crabby behaviour.

And then this whole thing about sex raises its ugly head at regular intervals. My partner reminds me that one day I will realise that there is more to life than sex. What I have realised is that there is more to sex than you had ever imagined, particularly in the case of men and women of a certain age! But no man wants to talk about sex and the menopausal woman. We prefer to live in a world of sexy lingerie, stockings and suspenders.

I had a strange dream the other day. My partner told me that we were going for a drive in the car. I offered to drive but she told me that she wanted to be in the driving seat. I dutifully took my place in the passenger seat. I did not recognise the road that we were on. I asked her where we were going. She replied, 'Don't worry. I'm in control. I'm taking you on the menopause road to Heaven.' The ride got bumpier. We were climbing up a steep and narrow mountain path. She changed gear. I started to nod off. She slammed on the brakes. We had taken a wrong turn. She reversed. We were now racing downhill. I couldn't figure out what the hell was going on. I looked at her. She was wearing black stockings and the red lingerie that I had bought her for Christmas. 'Are we nearly there?' I asked. 'You need to be patient,' she said with a smile on her face. I turned on the CD player. The refrain of a song by the Groove Factory filled the air. 'Let's talk about sex, baby, let's talk about you and me, let's talk all about the good things and the bad things that may be...' And then I woke up! My partner was not next to me in bed. Her night sweats had obviously forced her to seek refuge in the guest bedroom. I was initially afraid to tell my partner about the dream that I had because she is already convinced that I have a one track mind. One night, after several glasses of wine I plucked up the courage to tell her. I was surprised by her reaction. She just roared with laughter. I haven't seen her laugh like that for a long time.

Alas, those erotic images of sex and frantic love-making that we fantasise about and see in the movies have become clouded with images of 'being all dried up, lubricants, scheduling sex into your weekly routine, and losing that sense of spontaneity...' The reality is that the menopause forces both men and women to move out of their comfort zone when it comes to sex. My partner has realised that 'if she doesn't want to lose it, she has to use it'. And those men who tell you that they are having sex just as much as they used to when they were younger are either very lucky or being economical with the truth. Sex with a menopausal woman requires patience, understanding, patience and more patience! It generally requires a willingness on the part of the man to modify his approach to the sexual act. It requires a lot of effort and adjustment. It is no wonder that some men end up going off with a younger woman.

My partner wonders how celebrities like Demi Moore, Susan Sarandon, Goldie Hawn and Madonna are dealing with the menopause. We men are so busy looking at their physical appearance that we forget that these women must also have to manage the challenges of menopause. My partner is convinced that these famous women use hormone therapy. And let's be honest – these women have the financial means to get the best medical advice and help. They do not represent 'normal' women.

I have come to realise that being sympathetic towards your partner during her menopause years is the key to maintaining a happy relationship, both sexual and emotional. I am learning just how important it is for a man and his partner to have a very strong emotional bond during the menopause years. I feel that both partners must be willing to embrace and accept the changes that come with 'mid-life'. My partner keeps on reminding me that we should not try to recapture our youth. 'You can't be lamb again when you are mutton. And you can't be a Labrador puppy again when you are a seven-year-old Labrador! But no matter what your age, you can still have the charm of a lamb and the playfulness of a puppy.'

I hope my partner and I will remember that, irrespective of age, life is to be enjoyed. We may not be able to turn the biological clock back but we can still have fun at every stage of life. I tell myself that we must remember to make each other laugh and that I must learn to grow old gracefully.

Male menopause is a lot more fun than female menopause. With female menopause you gain weight and get hot flushes. With male menopause you get to date young girls and ride motorcycles.

(author unknown)

Nicholas, 50

There's no doubt the menopause is one of those mysterious things that can creep into a marriage – not a potential deal-breaker like the discovery of a hidden secret, but an irritant which in our case could have been fatal, as I shall explain. Even the word itself conveys a certain threat. The menopause, 'a pause from men': 'Oh ****!'

So there is no watershed moment, like the death of a favourite pet, announcing the arrival of trauma in one's life. It is just a vague appreciation that something is not quite right, that your partner is not quite herself and is struggling to make sense of the cause.

This, of course, is one of the key reasons why the menopause is so difficult to handle. While it seems to relate to a tangible event, i.e. the ceasing of menstruation, most men are probably only aware of minor physical symptoms exhibited by their partner. These can readily be put to the back of your mind given that you, as the man, are not experiencing them yourself. And in our busy lives, driven by deadlines and firefighting in the work environment, it is so easy not to provide your partner with the support and understanding she needs. 'So what if you're going to the toilet more often, darling? I'm really pissed off with my colleagues at work because they're not pulling their weight... There's not much I can do about your night sweats, love. It's been a crap day and we lost that deal I was telling you about...'

But just imagine if you were experiencing those symptoms yourself. Would you be able to shrug them off so lightly? Just think of the difference between 'ordinary flu' and 'man flu' –

my goodness, how we men would suffer if we had to go through the symptoms of the female menopause!

I suppose the realisation that a natural conception is no longer possible because of the menopause can have a profound impact on some women. But I rather suspect that, in most cases, this most fundamental consequence is of less concern than the undesirable side effects such as hot flushes and night sweats. After all, by the time of the menopause most women will either have conceived a sufficient number of times or already come to terms with the fact that it is not to be. In our case it was regretfully the latter, but the emotional difficulties that revolved around failed IVF treatments occurred a fair time before my wife's menopause began. But again, I just came to terms with the failure of IVF. How can I ever be certain that my wife did not continue to nurture a faint hope of conceiving, a hope that was to be finally extinguished when she went through the menopause? What a severe blow: final confirmation that there is no going back.

There have been so many advances in medical science in recent years that we have come to expect that treatment will be available when we develop a particular condition or ailment. The menopause is no exception. I don't mean in terms of delaying its onset, but in terms of alleviating some of those troublesome symptoms that a woman and her partner have become familiar with. In common with most women, my wife was aware that HRT can be helpful and went to see a consultant gynaecologist to discuss the different drugs that are available. I can't claim to have been active in this process, but I entirely understand why my wife decided to commence HRT.

It is my understanding that the primary objective of HRT is to boost oestrogen levels in the body. While HRT seems relatively benign, the consequences can be more serious. My wife had previously undergone surgery to remove lumps from her breast and, a couple of years after commencing HRT, she was diagnosed with breast cancer. Of course no one can be certain of the causal link, but I would just like to present one piece of evidence.

When she went into hospital to have an exploratory slice of tissue examined, the breast surgeon told us that he would be able to tell the extent of the cancer straight away. We were surprised to be told subsequently that they wanted to check again the following morning. When the consultant finally gave us the result of the biopsy, he said the reason why they had delayed was that they feared there had been a mix-up in samples taken from different women, since the frequency of cell divisions in my wife's sample was that of a 20-something woman. I am convinced this 'unnatural' cell activity was a consequence of the stimulus provided by HRT, and as far as I am concerned, therein lies one of its key risks. If you are encouraging a body that has already shown some signs of unnatural cell activity to develop new cells more rapidly than before, then inevitably it increases the chance that a rogue cell will be created.

I am no medic, but I feel strongly about this. It is of course understandable that women are tempted by HRT, and if you are lucky, it can be of significant benefit. But overall, I think the potential risks, which can be life threatening, are more important and should not be ignored. Also I have some suspicions about a branch of medicine which presumably has close ties with the drug companies that develop the competing products. It can distort a balanced assessment of whether to prescribe or not.

Thankfully my wife survived her breast cancer. She discontinued the HRT and her body is currently healthy, if a little heavier than before. From time to time I remind my wife that she needs to pay more attention to her diet and health. But hang on there, the words 'pot', 'kettle' and 'black' are springing to mind ... another Indian takeaway and a few pints of beer anyone?

I looked at myself in the mirror this morning. I seem to be developing a beer gut. I really must go to the gym more often. But things at work are just so hectic these days ... there is a recruitment freeze ... I'm working longer hours ... this is the worst recession we've seen since the 1930s ... I wonder if my pension pot will allow me to retire before the age of 60 ... I hope my wife is not going to be in one of her 'moods' when I get home...

We think in generalities but we live in details.

(Alfred North Whitehead)

James, 52

Putting into words how I feel about the menopause is not easy, because it involves a journey in which I am a somewhat helpless passenger. I feel I have no control over the numerous twists and turns which it has taken so far and which I will undoubtedly be confronted with over the next few years.

I have been married to my wife for 21 years. I had known her for ten years before that, so I feel as though we know each other extremely well. We have spent virtually the whole of our adult lives together. We have shared many great moments and a few not so good ones. We have similar tastes and we share a lot in common.

We have both worked hard to obtain what we have today. We both appreciate the fruits of our hard labour. For the past 30 years we have done virtually everything together, through thick and thin. The menopause, however, has in some ways interrupted the 'togetherness' we have enjoyed. We are still happily married, but our relationship has changed from what it used to be. When I think about it, the change started a few years ago, before I even became aware of the term 'the menopause'.

My wife had been on the Pill for a long time. She had started to complain about feeling tired and generally not very well. Her doctor suggested that she change the mix and strength of the Pill she was taking as she was at that age where she probably needed to change her contraceptive. This was about three years before my wife finally started the menopause and I will remember this period as the beginning of 'my journey into the unknown'.

My wife tried a couple of different contraceptive pills, but none of them agreed with her. She started to experience a range of mood swings. The mood swings started a year or two after she decided to leave her job in the City of London and pursue a new career. A career change had not been an easy decision for her at the time, but was inevitable as her work was affecting her health. She had my full support in that decision, as I could see how her job was having a deleterious effect on her.

At the time I was not sure if her change in moods was down to her decision to change profession, or whether it could be attributed to changes in the contraceptive pill that she was taking. I knew she was struggling with her change in status in life, because she is an independent person who wants to be self-supportive. She was now more reliant on me for money. That was hard for her to accept.

I felt mixed emotions, since for the first time in a long time I was struggling to understand why my wife was feeling the way she was. Was it the Pill, or was it the fact that she had changed professions, or was it a mixture of the two?

At this stage I was battling with my own emotions, and did not want to show it. So I am sure I probably appeared as uncaring and selfish. I had no idea how to react to the changes in my wife. To be frank, as a man, I found it hard to cope. In such situations I have a tendency to lock my feelings away and not show them, which with hindsight was perhaps not the way to behave. But that is the way I am.

Although my wife was on the Pill, because of the way she was feeling our sex life fell away to the extent that it was non-existent. As a man I found this state of affairs hard to grapple with. Do I discuss it with my wife, or do I let it go and hope that matters improve if and when the doctor finds a Pill that works for her? If I try to discuss it, how will she react? Will it make things worse? Will we finish up moving further apart?

All these questions were going through my mind, but in the end I guess I took the easy route and remained silent on the fact that our sex life was unsatisfactory.

While my wife was still on the Pill she started to have intermittent periods, which I found odd as I had always thought the Pill helped to regulate the menstrual cycle. She struggled on with erratic periods, but eventually sought advice from the doctor, who told her, 'You have to expect this. You have been on the Pill for a very long time, so it is time either to come off it or to go on to HRT.' I thought, 'Great, what do we do now?'

At the time there was a lot of press coverage about the causal links between HRT and breast cancer. It also seemed that there was no one magic HRT pill, but rather a whole range of possible varieties with different concentrations of oestrogen and progesterone. It was potentially a question of hit or miss as to whether you would find a mix that was suitable.

There seemed to be plenty of clinical studies and anecdotal evidence on the advantages of taking HRT, namely stability of moods and, importantly for me as a man, higher libido. My wife had already been through the best part of three years trying out different varieties of the contraceptive pill which had not worked for her and which had caused all sorts of anxiety for both of us, not to mention the beginning of the change in our relationship and our sex life. Even though HRT could be a panacea, there was no certainty about this and, more importantly, side effects such as an increased risk of developing breast cancer could potentially be devastating.

My wife and I discussed the pros and cons of trying HRT and concluded that the decision was simple. She had been on the Pill for around 25 years, which in itself has dangers. There was no guarantee that the doctor would be able to prescribe an HRT pill the first time round that would have the desired effects of alleviating the way my wife was currently feeling. So we agreed that she would come off the contraceptive pill, refuse HRT and deal with the consequences.

This was a turning point for me, a final realisation that my wife was probably about to go into the menopause, but I had no idea what this meant.

What is the menopause? How does it manifest itself? How long does it last? I knew nothing, but then I did nothing to find out more about it either. All I knew, simplistically, was that my wife's childbearing years had come to an end. I wanted my wife to feel better. While I knew that refusing HRT was the right decision for her, it was probably going to make her feel worse in the short term. I would have to prepare myself for more ups and downs.

We are now four years into my wife's menopause and the process of change continues. There have been times when I feel as though I do not know my wife. Her mood changes so quickly, and she goes from being her normal self to being someone who I feel is hypercritical of me, for what appears at the time to be a non-event. I might respond to a question in a tone of voice which she immediately reacts to and then I have to sit through a lengthy criticism of the way I am behaving and how thoughtless and selfish I am. While I am not entirely blameless, it is often difficult to tune into what she is feeling. There are times when I am tired, having had a hard day at work. I admit that I may not be as considerate or thoughtful as she would like, but does this warrant such a reaction? I don't know. All I can say is that when it comes, her torrent of criticism is not pleasant. I just try to adjust my response or remain silent in the hope that she will stop having a go at me!

There have been occasions recently when I have seen the life literally drain away from my wife's face. One moment we could be having a normal conversation and then, without warning, she turns very pale and looks as white as a ghost. When this happens she just has to go to bed. That's scary.

Nothing can really prepare a man for the sweats that come in torrents to his partner during her menopause. I try to be understanding, but when we are having a quiet cuddle in bed, and the next moment I am covered in her perspiration, I move away and try to ignore what has just happened, even though what I really want is to hold her. But I just can't, because the closer our bodies are, the worse it gets!

Next to the sweats are all the disturbed nights due to the tossing and turning because she cannot sleep and because she is sweating so much!

Over a period of time all this takes its toll. I end up being tired not just from working hard at the office, but also from the fact that I am not getting a lot of sleep because my wife is not sleeping well.

Then we start to sleep in separate beds because that is the only way I can get a decent night's rest. I really do not like doing this, as it does not feel right if we are not in the same bed. We may not have any sex life, but at least we can sleep in the same bed.

The combination of the mood swings, reactions, tiredness, sweating, sleepless nights and ultimately not sleeping together does make you wonder where everything is leading. It doesn't end there, though, because mixed in with this, one learns about vaginal dryness and urinary tract infections. None of which you're prepared for. You begin to wonder: is it just us, or do other couples go through the same? But it is hardly the sort of topic you can bring up at the dinner table with your friends. So in the end you do not talk about it with anyone. As a man you just want it all to end and for life to go back to the way it was, before all the changes started. You want your partner to stop having to go through all the agony and unpleasantness.

Analysing all of this, you begin to understand why some couples who have been married for many years suddenly split up when they are in their late 40s and early 50s. You also begin to think that you understand why a man might go off with a younger woman because he can't cope with the stress of all the changes that his partner is going through. But then maybe things get worse because they do not discuss their feelings about how menopause is affecting their life!

In my case the worst period was probably the first 18 months of my wife's menopause, because I tended to stand back and, to a degree, I even tried to ignore what was happening in the hope that it would soon end. It did not and it still has not, after four years. After months of discord we started to talk more openly and freely about how my wife was really feeling and what she was going through. This helped, but the mood changes have continued to this day, albeit to a lesser degree.

My wife has a tendency to analyse situations, particularly ones she does not fully understand or control, so she searched the Internet for information on the menopause and bought books on the subject. At some point she read an article about how diet and exercise could help achieve a balance during the menopause. So she changed her diet and started to run regularly. Initially this had little or no effect. However, my wife persevered and gradually I could see she was achieving greater emotional balance, and at the same time was becoming extremely fit. The distances she ran grew from 5 to 10 to 15 and eventually 20 kilometres. Amazing! However, there have been times when I have worried that she is pushing herself too hard, leaving herself profoundly tired and drained of energy. I want to encourage her, but at the same time do not want her to get overtired.

The diet and running have been a great success, and after two or more years, my wife is able to listen to her body most of the time. She is learning not to go beyond the threshold where she starts undoing the good that running and exercise creates.

I think we have both learned to live with the menopause. Neither of us has any idea how much longer it will continue, nor if we will be faced with new challenges that neither of us is expecting.

There are still times when it is not easy for me to live with the menopause. My emotions boil up inside, but I say to myself that it will end one day.

I am determined to get through my wife's menopause with our relationship intact. It is not going to be easy, but life is not always easy, is it?

When one door of happiness closes, another opens: but often we look so long at the closed door that we do not see the one which has been opened for us.

(Helen Keller)

Simon, 55

My life revolves around my job and my family. My philosophy is to deal with challenges and problems as and when they arise. I take the view that a similar strategy should be applied to dealing with the menopause. It's pointless worrying about it before the event.

My wife recently celebrated her fiftieth birthday. I do not know if she is embarking on the menopause years. She has not discussed the subject with me. I am not familiar with the topic or the symptoms (other than the customary references to 'hot flushes' and 'cranky behaviour') that women are supposed to suffer from as a result of the menopause. If my wife is facing a health problem because of the menopause, I will encourage her to see my doctor, to whom I have access as a result of my private medical insurance. I have total confidence in my doctor. If he were to recommend that my wife use HRT, I would ask her to consider that option seriously. I would also encourage my wife to do as much research as possible about the menopause on the Internet. I think that the Internet is a wonderful tool because it enables people to be better informed.

Over the years I have come to accept that my wife is not very vocal about her health and has a tendency to suffer in silence if she has a health problem. I am the one who pushes her to seek medical advice if I feel that a physical or emotional ailment is turning into a crisis. I work on the principle that a health crisis for my wife will affect me in due course, so it is important for me to help her work through any health issues that she might be facing.

I believe that menopause, both female and male, is part and

59

parcel of the changes that couples go through during their married life. Marriage is a contract. I view it as a 'deal' that is entered into by husband and wife. The deal includes things like having children and agreeing on a division of responsibilities. For example, my wife and I have agreed that it is my role to go to work and earn money because I am better qualified to do so in our relationship. My wife's role is to be the homemaker and look after the children because she is better at that. The deal is based on the principle of working together 'for better or for worse'. My wife and I are both 'stakeholders' in our marriage. As stakeholders we have equal rights and obligations, both of which are important in order to make our 'association' a success. We need to listen to each other's point of view. We have to ensure that, as we approach our 'menopause years', we make time for each other. It is important not to allow our children and my job to be the only things that define our lives.

For me the analogy between marriage and owning a company is relevant because the long-term success of both depends on the stakeholders' ability to work towards a common goal, to adapt to changing circumstances and to air and debate any differences of opinion in a constructive manner. If the focus is on short-term goals and gratification of individuals' needs, the deal between the parties will ultimately break down.

My wife went through considerable emotional and physical change during pregnancy. I was there to support her. I will be there for her if she goes through any physical and emotional changes as a result of the menopause. I believe that good communication is the key to solving any problem, whether it relates to children, work, marriage, finances or, indeed, the menopause.

I hope my wife will talk to me about her feelings and any problems that she experiences during the menopause. If she does not, I will initiate the discussion if I feel that her symptoms are seriously beginning to affect our relationship and my life with her.

Life is full of change. Menopause, whether female or male, represents change. We have to learn to deal with change. And like all other things in life, some deal with it better than others.

Two monologues do not make a dialogue.

(Jeff Daly)

Richard, 58

I am self-employed. I have three teenage children and a dog. Private education and a relatively high standard of living are putting a strain on our finances. I have not made adequate provision for a pension. The economic downturn is not helping matters. I sometimes get panic attacks. My wife is 52. She is going through the menopause. I have added her menopause to my list of 'problems to deal with'.

My wife is always tired and complains that she is not feeling well. She is gaining weight. She suffers from migraines and constipation. Her personality seems to be changing. She went to see her doctor the other day. Results showed that she has high blood pressure, high cholesterol and problems with her thyroid. The doctor has given her a pamphlet about HRT.

My wife is increasingly finding fault with me. She never used to. She is moody and suffers from bouts of depression. Silly things make her depressed – like watching the news on TV. She complains that I don't help enough around the house. She seems constantly on edge. She says that I am self-centred and too 'needy'. She tells me that she is fed up with my problems at work. She thinks that my problems are self-inflicted because I am unwilling to lower my expectations about life and achievement. Is the menopause responsible for all this upheaval, or are we just going through a bad patch in our marriage?

I, too, am becoming more aware of her 'shortcomings'. For example, she is always late for appointments and cannot make a decision about anything without causing a drama or stress for the entire family.

My wife seems to have lost the ability to think rationally. Even the children are becoming impatient at her lack of organisation. She often has trouble getting the children to school on time.

Despite all this, she seems unwilling to lead a more balanced and structured lifestyle when it comes to looking after her body. She talks about the need for a lifestyle change and healthy living because of her menopause, but does not put this talk into action. She does not eat at regular intervals and stays up late into the night. She talks about doing more exercise, but never makes time for it. And I am invariably the one who gets the blame. Her answer to my accusations of poor planning and time-keeping on her part is that she would like a more 'random and relaxed' existence in her 50s. The children do not need her as much as they used to so she does not want to be a slave to routine any more! Not clever if she is suffering both physically and emotionally as a result of the menopause.

My wife's menopause has created tensions in our relationship. I have become conscious of the fact that we no longer want the same things in life. My wife seems to be hankering after a 'perfect life'. She wants a husband who is caring and attentive to her needs, believes in equality between the sexes, shares in the housework, does not travel overseas for work, is home for dinner at seven, spends quality time with the children, is less stressed and earns lots of money. Do you think that is a realistic expectation on her part?

My wife and I still have a few things in common. We are both idealistic and insecure. However, my idealism does not stop me from living and working in the 'big bad world' that surrounds us. My wife, on the other hand, does not want to have anything to do with the nasty world of commerce and finance. The world of commerce, however, is where I earn a living!

I applaud my wife for wanting the world to be a place where there is no poverty or conflict. She is outraged by injustice and the images of war. She vents her anger by becoming stressed and depressed. I feel as though I bear the brunt of these emotions. She thinks that people should be paid a fair wage for working, that we should keep our children safe from harm, and that we should look after the elderly. My wife believes that all food should be organically grown. We should cut down on waste. We should recycle our rubbish and reduce our carbon footprint. She can't fathom why most people in the business world are purely motivated by money. The menopause seems to have increased my wife's idealism. One of my teenage daughters asked her the other day why, instead of becoming depressed about the state of the world, she doesn't do something proactive about improving the awful world we live in. Like working on an aid project in Africa for six months. *That* did not go down terribly well!

My wife has never had a permanent job. She hates working amongst people who do not think like her or share her value system. She misinterprets other people's views and comments as a criticism of her way of life. She never used to be like that. She is aware that she lacks confidence and blames her parents. She blames her parents for having low expectations of her. Our parents have a hand in shaping our personality, but we can't blame them for everything!

My wife criticises me for being obsessive about work and stressed about income generation. But she still wants and needs all the creature comforts that money can buy. I worry about the size of our mortgage and how I am going to pay for holidays.

If I have one of my panic attacks, my wife reminds me that we could live on a lot less and 'downsize' if necessary.

My wife seems totally dissatisfied with me and with life. I

know I should be more sympathetic to the changes that she is going through as a result of the menopause, but I am finding it very hard. I sometimes wish she would go and work on an aid project in Africa in order to get all this negative energy and frustration out of her system! Aid work might make her realise just how lucky she is.

If I complain about our finances, she reminds me that she can get a part-time job of some description if I feel that I cannot earn enough income to support our family. Being an alpha male, this makes me feel inadequate and a failure. I remind my wife that she doesn't have a professional qualification so she would not be able to earn very much. This is probably not a very tactful thing to say. I was brought up to believe that it is a man's role to provide for his wife and children. My ego prevents me from admitting that I am struggling financially. I want my wife to 'offer' to go to work rather than insisting that she goes to work because we have a large overdraft.

I do not have the courage to tell her that she needs to get a grip, take control of her menopause symptoms and figure out what she really wants in life because I am tired of trying to figure it out for her. I am tired of 'picking up the pieces' and being a constant pillar of strength. Has the menopause turned my wife into someone who is incapable of living in and dealing with the real world? Perhaps I should encourage her to try HRT. All these thoughts are buzzing through my head as my wife sinks deeper into menopause.

My wife and I seem to be leading parallel lives. We have drifted apart. In my most insecure moments I wonder whether she stays with me because the children are still at home and because she needs me to support her financially. Would she leave me if I suddenly became a multi-millionaire? Would she take the kids and half my wealth? I suppose I should thank my wife's menopause for forcing me to take stock of my life.

My wife and I had a frank discussion the other day. She feels that she has always been there to support me during the 'tough times', of which there have been many during my working life. She says that my ups and downs have always taken priority over her needs. She can't live like that any more. Since she is 'suffering' as a result of the menopause; it is time for me to give priority to her needs. We, or rather I, have decided that I need to make some compromises.

So I have agreed to a change in my daily routine. I work more from home. Because she is always tired and finds it difficult to get up in the morning, I take the kids to school. I walk the dog if she doesn't want to. I see more of her friends and family than mine. But despite all my efforts, my wife still does not seem happier.

She has started an Open University course, but is finding it difficult to keep up with the course work. She has started working for a couple of hours a week. She now complains that her course work and her paid employment are causing stress and not leaving her enough time to do the things she enjoys. She is not sure if she has made the right decision in taking on study and work commitments. She complains that she does not have time to do fun things with the children. She has no time for decorating projects around the house. My children and I have noticed that my wife has become obsessive about trivial things around the house. She never used to be like that. What has the menopause done to the woman I married? Is my wife having a 'breakdown', or should I blame the menopause for this transformation?

I am trying to maintain a positive attitude despite the extra pressure that I feel as a result of the 'new deal' at home between my wife and me. I have recently even had a couple of therapy sessions. My therapist and I have talked mainly about my childhood and how it has affected my behaviour, my thought patterns, my expectations and my working life. I have not as yet felt comfortable about talking to my therapist about my wife's menopause. Perhaps it is my wife who needs therapy.

I sometimes wonder if I am feeling unsettled because I, too, am going through the menopause – the 'male' variety, that is. I often think of my advancing age and my own mortality. I have this burning desire to experience new and exciting adventures before I turn 60, before it is too late. I want to go trekking in Africa, climb a mountain, write a book, discover my roots. I can't see how I am going to fulfil these dreams. Financial obligations and family commitments are holding me back. When I talk to my children about my desire for adventure, my 13-year-old son tells me to 'get real' and reminds me that I must be going through a 'mid-life crisis'!

I haven't read any books about the menopause. I really don't have the time or the inclination to do so. I am left wondering if my wife and I will pull through all of this with our relationship intact. I hope she decides to give HRT a go. I take the view that if the benefits outweigh the risks, it must be worth a try. Life is full of calculated risk. Shouldn't my wife consider the 'risk ratio' in making a decision on whether or not to use HRT? But it is not *my* body that is going through a change, so I have to let my wife make her own choice on HRT.

I am sure many couples experience difficulties during middle age and menopause. People seem reluctant to talk about 'private' matters such as menopause, because they feel that others might criticise them for washing their dirty linen in public or laugh at them behind their backs. I should really find the courage to talk to my therapist and male friends about it. My friends might be having similar experiences. That might make me feel better! They might even be able to give me some advice on how to deal with a few of my problems. Next Friday evening at the pub maybe...

In the meantime, I am grateful that I have a dog. We go for very long walks at the weekend. I often tell my dog about my frustrations and how I am feeling. He never offers advice, never answers back or questions my judgement. He is easy to please and is never moody. He never has teenage tantrums or complains about my work commitments. I always feel much happier after a walk with my dog. Who needs a therapist when you have a dog?

Each of us will suffer at different points in our lives, and when we are married, we are committed to sharing the pain of another person.

(Norman Wright)

Andrew, 63

I like to refer to the female menopause as the 'conventional menopause'. If you were to mention these two words to a man in his 20s or 30s, you would undoubtedly be greeted with a bored expression on his face. The topic would be of little or no interest to him. By the time that man reaches the age of 50, his attitude to this word will have changed, especially if he is married to a woman of a similar age or older, or if he is unmarried but is in a relationship with someone of the opposite sex who has reached that 'critical age'.

It is a well-known fact that for women, there are significant changes in their bodies and even their minds as they age. After reaching puberty in their teens, they move on to their actual or potential childbearing age and then they go through this awkward period of the menopause: hot flushes, uneven temperament and a difficult phase of physical change and emotional adjustment. They finally move on to act and behave and, eventually, look more like their mother! What is interesting for the observant male, however, is how many women in their age of menopause positively bloom and become more sexually attractive. It is difficult to explain why this situation arises. It does not seem to be dependent on how old or how young the observing man is. To my mind, this is perhaps one of the mysteries and contradictory experiences of the female menopause.

For the man who lives with a woman going through the menopause, it is also a difficult period. Not only is the woman getting older, but more importantly she is also changing in her attitude to sexuality. Her keenness for an active sexual relationship can reduce, sometimes significantly. She may still want to please her man sexually, but she finds it more difficult to be as enthusiastic as she was earlier in her life. The man may still be as keen as ever, but for him his partner's apparent change makes the sexual act a much less satisfying experience. Some men also ease off in their sexual interest and desires as they age, while others seem to stay the same. Yet others become even keener, perhaps aware that their sexual prowess may be declining. In my case I am as keen as I ever was!

The problem can be that, when you discover your sexual partner is not always as keen as you, and at the vital moment 'heats up' and even sweats profusely, it can be a bit of a turn-off for the man. Everything seems fine and then suddenly it starts. There is no warning. It is perhaps as much of a shock to the woman as it is to the man. I suspect that even the keenest male athlete would find this phenomenon of the overheating woman a significant problem, making the sexual encounter much less satisfying than he had imagined or perhaps hoped.

I have come to believe that this problem of the older female heating up was part of God's cunning plan for our ancestors to move the ageing male on to new sexual exploits with younger women. It was a way of ensuring the continuity of new and healthier offspring at a time when child mortality was much higher than it is today. Could it also be Nature's clever plan for survival of the species? It may explain why today, more older and even ageing men move on to replace their long-established partner with a younger model. I do not recommend or condone this action, but merely offer an explanation as to why it seems widespread and even acceptable in many societies.

A lot has been written about the female menopause, but what is not often publicised or openly discussed is the subject of the male menopause. Like women, men also age, but in different ways. I think both men and women need to accept that there *is* such a thing as male menopause. I feel that male menopause is even more of a taboo subject than female menopause. Male menopause is not something that I have ever discussed with male colleagues or friends. Males are proud beasts and are always reluctant to admit to weaknesses. Like lions prowling around in the jungle or on the plain, the last thing that we want to admit to in front of a 'fellow lion' is something that might be embarrassing. I can only speak from experience. It is possible that men who are about ten years younger than me speak more freely about such things with each other. Somehow, though, I doubt it!

Based on my own experience and observations of other men who are of a similar age to me, I am totally convinced that men go through a menopause phase. How long it lasts I cannot tell, but from personal experience, it starts around the age of 55. Men do not experience the severity of symptoms that women have to face as a result of hormonal changes and loss of fertility. A man's symptoms seem to be more emotional than physical.

For some inexplicable reason, the male menopause can cause a man to run completely off the rails. He sets aside all sense of logic and reason and gets dragged down into some illusion that life will become much better outside his established set of relationships. He is prepared to wreck his family life, run into debt, set aside his religious beliefs – not always for a younger woman (or perhaps a relationship with a man), but to set up house with another woman of his own age. So this situation is not one of the male setting off to find another younger woman to start a new family, as some might often imagine. It is more a crisis that is brought about by an unfortunate set of circumstances – perhaps changing a job, losing a job, or transformation from apparent success to failure at that critical time of life just before the age of 60, which, incidentally, I think is the height of the male menopause. Everything becomes too much for the man. He feels misunderstood. He feels neglected. He feels undervalued. He tries to escape from reality.

The male menopause seems to relate to the man's sense of 'fading' and the significant onset of the ageing process. The gradual eclipse of his capabilities as a man, especially his physical strength, can become a problem. Suddenly the stamina of an 18-year-old boy has gone and the man now feels tired after a long day or a sustained period of effort. As a consequence his mind starts to wander and, worse still, he can find himself drifting away from his traditional relationships in an erroneous effort to try to recapture his youth.

In my case this has not been a major problem, but I have noticed that for some other men I know, the situation has led to disaster. Take, for example, what recently happened to a close friend of mine. He had a good job in a company that he had seen grow significantly through his own hard work. His family history was of a stable and apparently happy marriage. He had two children at university. He was one of the pillars of his local Christian church. One day he decided to leave his job and join a new start-up consulting and asset management company in the City of London. This job started well, but then the financial crisis of 2008 erupted and this changed everything. The main shareholder supporting the new business decided to pull the plug and the company was shut down, resulting in my friend losing his job.

The consequences of his loss of employment and difficulty in securing another position caused a complete breakdown in his relationships at home. He fell out with his two children and left his wife and moved in with a former girlfriend whom he had earlier intended to marry, prior to meeting the woman who became his wife. His wife and children were distraught at this turn of events. His wife thought they had a good marriage of 30 years' standing. She begged him to come back. She would forgive everything. His daughter was due to get married and refused to be given away by her itinerant father. His son had a breakdown and had to leave university. All his friends advised him to go back home to his wife. At first he seemed willing to listen to his friends. Then he started turning down agreed meetings at the last minute, saying that 'something important had cropped up'.

I put all of this down to the male menopause. Would the outcome have been different if he or his wife had considered the possibility that he was going through the male menopause and sought guidance and support from qualified medical professionals to get him through this phase in his life? Our society does not encourage men to be open about their insecurities. We judge men who admit to feelings of inadequacy and insecurity as weak individuals. While some companies now offer their male employees 'lifestyle coaching' as they reach retirement age, most men are left to their own devices when it comes to accepting loss of youth and preparation for retirement and senior citizenship.

In today's stressful world, the ambitious male feels that he has to demonstrate continuous success even where his partner would be content with less. It is often difficult for the man to accept that he has peaked and is now moving into decline. This is especially so if the man feels he could have done better financially and in career terms, and perhaps feels that he has been denied the opportunities that should have come to him through a combination of merit and endeavour. Faced with emotions that are brought on by the male menopause, he loses a sense of balance and, in the worst cases, all sense of realism. Suddenly the world outside with a new partner seems much more attractive than staying within the boundaries of an existing marriage. This might all be an illusion or a dreadful mistake, but the man loses all sense of reason and responsibility. He embarks on a new adventure. When things don't work out, it is often too late to rectify matters, so he buries his head in the sand and pretends that everything is all right. He does not examine the underlying reasons for the changes that have occurred.

Today a large number of marriages and stable long-term relationships involving men aged 55 and over break up when the man walks out to set up a completely new set of friendships and relationships. I am not talking about the callous male who has little long-term concern for his wife or long-standing partner, his family and his friends. The male I refer to is the caring, apparently loving type who normally values his family, friends and acquaintances. But he decides to throw all these things away. He is happy to take this type of risk, which he would not have done ten years earlier. Is the little voice in his head encouraging him to throw caution to the wind and experience new things before it is too late? Is it the male menopause that is egging him on to behave in this way?

So is the male menopause an 'emotional condition'? Is emotional turmoil its main characteristic? Are men totally exempt from physical symptoms? My own experience suggests otherwise. Men too can experience physical discomfort, but probably not to the extent experienced by women. I am not referring here to things like high blood pressure, heart disease, osteoporosis or ill health caused by poor diet or stress. I am referring to physical symptoms that are not harmful to a man's health. For example, I find it hard to believe that I am the only man of a certain age to experience 'heat and airlessness', both inside and outside. I experience these in a way that was hardly noticeable before the age of 55. It is a bizarre feeling and difficult to put into words. My consciousness of the environment, especially within my body, has become much more apparent than it ever was when I was much younger. Nobody seems willing to talk about this strange phenomenon, and to the best of my knowledge, nobody has written about it. Am I the only man alive to experience this? I think not!

Another physical symptom that I have experienced is what I like to call 'temperature runaways'. Suddenly, for no reason, I start to feel hot and then very hot. My body temperature seems to rise for no explicable reason. My body feels hotter and hotter. Then, just as suddenly, it stops. It does not happen very often. Also it is impossible to predict when this type of event will occur. It does not happen at regular intervals. It seems to come always at awkward times during the day, never at night. Although it only lasts a few minutes, the experience for a man is most unpleasant, as though one is completely out of control. There seems to be no readily available explanation for this phenomenon and I have not had the courage to discuss it with anyone. The only benefit so far is that it has never happened during the sexual act, so at least I have never had the embarrassing experience of explaining this condition to my wife! Compared to the female menopause and women's experience of hot flushes, the male equivalent is a much more trivial matter. It is more like 'hot flashes' than 'hot flushes'! Nevertheless, it does seem to exist and at least, in my case, it is an annoying experience.

I have tried to describe the characteristics of the male menopause as candidly as I can, because I feel that men are reluctant to 'go there'. I believe that men, like women, also suffer from a menopause and should speak out. As is the case with women, male menopause can have major effects on a man's character and his life. While the male menopause is not the only reason for a mid-to-late-life crisis in the lives of many men, I feel that it can be a major contributory factor, causing an otherwise sensible and caring male to enter into acts of complete folly.

If my supposition of the existence of the male menopause is true, then we and society all need to take this into account in order to ensure that circumstances do not conspire and lead the male to behave out of character or to destroy his family situation. Men should not feel embarrassed and emasculated if they seek help or admit that they cannot cope with their emotions or the loss of youth. With specialist counselling, men might be able to achieve greater balance in their life during the male menopause years. For some, the misery of a family break-up could be avoided.

As is the case with the female menopause, we now need to acknowledge the changing situation of the male in modern Western society and help him to come to terms with, and to cope with, the ageing process. Like the female menopause, the male menopause can last a significant number of years. Men need to face up to this fact. The age of male macho invincibility is over. Like women, men are also weak and vulnerable. We need to acknowledge that 'male menopause' is not a derogatory term. The male menopause is a period of transition and change during which a man is riddled with emotions.

Life is full of change. Menopause is just one of those changes. Male menopause is not a 'medical condition'. We men can give whatever name we like to this stage of our life. I am happy to refer to it as the male menopause – it does not take away my manhood! So why are we so unwilling to admit that it might exist?

Deal with the faults of others as gently as with your own.

(Chinese proverb)

Things your father should have told you when you turned 40!

- For the woman in your life, menopause will be as significant an event as puberty.
- Her menopause will become your challenge.
- Don't give up on her.
- Ask her how she is feeling. Don't switch off when she starts talking about the menopause!
- If you are not coping with life events and her menopause, open up, tell her how you feel. Remember, she is not a mind reader.
- Close your eyes for a moment and imagine what it must feel like to have hot flushes, night sweats and have 'private bits' that are all dried up!
- Buy her flowers, cook her dinner. Put the bins out. Offer to do the shopping. Don't wait till she asks you to do these things. It kind of defeats the object of the exercise if she has to ask you.
- Don't expect sex to be as frequent and as spontaneous as it used to be. If that is what you want you will have to work at it. That will be another challenge!
- Don't blame her menopause for everything that is not quite right in your life as you embark on middle age.
- Life is full of compromises. You can't always have your cake and eat it too.
- Laughter is the best medicine during middle age.

Books for him

Goodman, Michael P., *Men-opause: The Book for Men* (Bandon, Oregon: Robert D. Reed Publishers, 2008).

Northrup, Dr Christiane, *The Wisdom of Menopause: The Complete Guide to Creating Physical and Emotional Health and Healing* (London: Piatkus, 2001). With this one, it might be better just to give him the pages that you would like him to read, not the whole book!

Definitions for him

Pre-menopause

A woman's reproductive years are coming to an end. You will know because she will complain about irregular periods. But take precautions. She could still get pregnant! You don't want accidents, do you?

Peri-menopause

The time between pre-menopause and menopause. Her hormone levels will be all over the place. Amongst other things, expect crabby behaviour, hot flushes, sweating at night, insomnia, fatigue, memory loss *and* lower sex drive! Not much to look forward to for either of you.

Menopause

Literally means the end of monthly cycles, the end of fertility in a woman. Sometimes referred to as 'the climateric', from the Greek word 'klimacter' which means 'critical period'. Heralds the end of egg production by a woman's ovaries. You may remember this definition from your biology or sex education lessons at school.

Post menopause

Oestrogen levels and levels of other hormones continue to drop. Increased risk of cardiovascular disease, osteopenia and osteoporosis. She needs to take care of her health. So do you!

Osteopenia

A wake-up call. First signs of low bone density. She needs to improve her nutrition and may need to take medication for this condition.

Osteoporosis

A significant loss of bone mineral density and increased risk of fractures. Not good news for either you or her.

This is a tough time. Hormones really begin to rock 'n roll here, and your partner may feel like a puppet on a string, jerked around by forces outside her control. OUTSIDE OF HER CONTROL!

(Michael P Goodman, *Menopause, The Book For Men,* p. 4)

Author's Note

Benjamin Franklin once said that 'in this world nothing is certain but death and taxes'. I would like to add a third item at the end of this quote: 'death and taxes and menopause'!

As I continue to reflect on the menopause and life I ask myself if the physical symptoms, the insomnia and the uncontrollable mood swings that I have encountered during my menopause are of a hormonal nature or whether they are related to my psychological make-up and life experiences. Has my lifestyle been a major contributory factor? Or is it my gene pool that is responsible for my hormonal disharmony? I cannot be certain about any of these factors but I am sure about one thing. We cannot control the genetic make-up we inherit at birth or the cultural, social and financial circumstances that we are born into. Similarly, some changes that we face in life are not within our control. However, as adults, we can make choices on how we react to our background and our blueprint. We can also make choices on how to respond to changes in our personal circumstances.

My discussions with men and women about the menopause have taught me that there should be no battle between the sexes when it comes to middle age and the menopause. Women and men need to listen to each other's point of view and reflect on how our upbringing, our culture, our education and our anatomy are responsible for shaping our views on this time of life.

There are millions of women who are currently going through

the menopause, or who will experience it in the not-too-distant future. Many do not have the time or the financial means to address the reasons behind the physical and emotional changes that they might be experiencing during their menopause years. For others, their upbringing, their social and cultural environment, or the man in their life may not encourage them to explore or expose their feelings about the menopause. I hope this book will serve as a prop for such women.

I hope my book of reflections will encourage women to develop a more positive attitude towards the menopause and view the menopause as a gift from Nature rather than a curse. I hope it will convince them that menopause need not be a taboo subject. I hope it will galvanise them into actively seeking, perhaps even demanding, a better quality of life as they embark on their menopause years.

Finally, I hope *Menopause Confidential* will bring a smile to the faces of both women and men because they will realise that they are not alone in the way they feel!